YOU ASKED FOR IT, CHARLIE BROWN

Selected cartoons from
You're The Guest Of Honour,
Charlie Brown, Vol. 2

Charles M. Schulz

CORONET BOOKS
Hodder Fawcett, London

First published by Fawcett
Publications Inc., New York

Coronet edition 1979

Printed in Great Britain for Hodder
Fawcett Ltd., Mill Road, Dunton Green,
Sevenoaks, Kent (Editorial Office: 47
Bedford Square, London WC1 3DP) by
C. Nicholls & Company Ltd
The Philips Park Press, Manchester

ISBN 0 340 23236 6

The Bunnies-A Tale of Mirth and Woe.

"Ha Ha Ha," laughed the bunnies.

"Ha Ha Ha Ha Ha Ha Ha Ha Ha Ha Ha Ha"

SO MUCH FOR THE MIRTH!

I'M SORT OF CURIOUS ABOUT SOMETHING..

DO YOU THINK YOU'LL EVER GET MARRIED, CHUCK?

OH, I SUPPOSE SO...JUST ABOUT EVERYONE DOES...

WHAT KIND OF GIRL DO YOU THINK YOU'LL MARRY?

WELL, I ALWAYS KIND OF HATE TO TALK ABOUT THOSE THINGS BECAUSE IT MAY SOUND SILLY, BUT I'D LIKE A GIRL WHO WOULD CALL ME, "POOR, SWEET BABY"

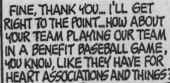

IF WE'RE GOING TO HAVE A CHARITY BASEBALL GAME, CHARLIE BROWN, IT SHOULD BE FOR A WORTHY CAUSE..

HOW ABOUT HEADACHES? NO ONE EVER HAS A BENEFIT FOR HEADACHES...

HOW ABOUT SORE THROATS? OR HOW ABOUT CUT FINGERS AND SKINNED KNEES?

IF OUR TEAM IS GOING TO BE PLAYING, IT SHOULD BE FOR STOMACH-ACHES!

I CAN'T STAND IT!

JUST THINK, CHUCK, OUR CHARITY BASEBALL GAME IS NEXT WEEK!

I'M VERY EXCITED... I THINK IT'S GOING TO BE THE BIGGEST THING EVER!

YOU AND YOUR STUPID BALL GAME! HAVE YOU EVER TRIED TO SELL TICKETS TO A STOMACH-ACHE?!!

NOBODY WANTS TO COME TO YOUR STUPID OL' BALL GAME! I'M TIRED OF HAVING DOORS SLAMMED IN MY FACE!!

I COULD HAVE BEEN MUGGED! A STOMACH-ACHE IS NO KIND OF CHARITY! I HATE SELLING TICKETS! I HATE BASEBALL!

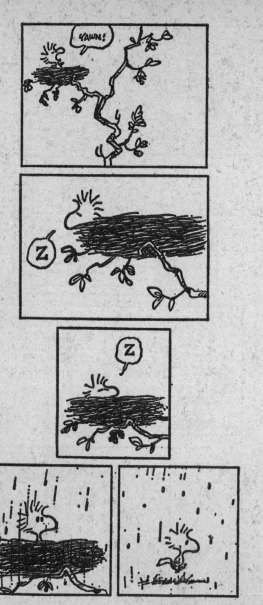

"Hi, pretty girl," he said.

"I love you," she said, and together they laughed. Then one day she said, "I hate you," and they cried. But not together.

"What happened to the love that we said would never die?" she asked. "It died," he said.

The first time he saw her she was playing tennis. The last time he saw her she was playing tennis.

"Ours was a Love set," he said, "but we double-faulted." "You always talked a better game than you played," she said.

THAT'S VERY GOOD...NOW ALL YOU NEED IS A TITLE...

A Love Story by Erich Beagle

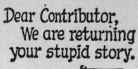

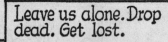

TODAY IS FATHER'S DAY...

I WONDER WHERE MY FATHER IS...

THAT'S THE TROUBLE WITH BEING A DOG... THEY TAKE YOU AWAY FROM YOUR FAMILY, AND SELL YOU TO SOME STUPID KID AND YOU NEVER SEE YOUR MOM AND DAD AGAIN!

"BUT YOU GET TO LIVE WITH A HUMAN FAMILY," THEY SAY... HA! BIG DEAL! SOME CHOICE!

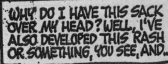

WHAT ARE YOU PACKING FOR, BIG BROTHER?

MY DOCTOR SAYS I SHOULD GO TO CAMP...HE SAID I HAVE TO DO SOMETHING THAT WILL TAKE MY MIND OFF BASEBALL

I'VE SEEN YOU PLAY... I NEVER THOUGHT YOU HAD YOUR MIND ON IT!

THANKS A LOT... I'LL SEE YOU IN TWO WEEKS...

YOU'RE GOING TO BE A BIG HIT AT CAMP CARRYING YOUR HEAD IN A SACK!!

SCHULZ

SO HERE I AM ON A BUS GOING TO CAMP...

FOR SOMEONE WHO HATES GOING TO CAMP, I SURE SPEND A LOT OF TIME THERE...MAYBE I WENT TO THE WRONG DOCTOR...

EVERY SUMMER HE DRAGS HIS FAMILY OFF ON A FIVE-WEEK CAMPING TRIP...HIS SOLUTION FOR EVERYTHING IS "GO TO CAMP!"

I KNOW WHAT'LL HAPPEN TO ME.. JUST WHEN I GET OLD ENOUGH WHERE I WON'T HAVE TO GO ANY MORE, I'LL GET DRAFTED INTO THE INFANTRY!

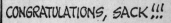

Y'KNOW, SACK, THAT WASN'T A BAD BREAKFAST

I WAS HERE LAST YEAR, AND THE FOOD WAS TERRIBLE!

I'LL BET YOU STRAIGHTENED THEM OUT, DIDN'T YOU, SACK? I'LL BET YOU TOLD THEM TO SHAPE UP ON THE FOOD HERE, OR SHIP OUT, DIDN'T YOU?

YOU'RE A GOOD CAMP PRESIDENT, SACK!

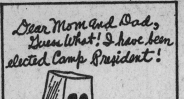

YEARS AGO THERE WAS A CARTOON DRAWN BY FRANK WING ABOUT FISHING...

THIS BOY WAS HELPING HIS DAD HOE THE GARDEN, AND HE SAID, "GEE, PA, I'LL BET THE FISH ARE BITIN' GOOD TODAY," AND HIS DAD SAID, "UH HUH, AN' IF YOU STAY WHERE YOU'RE AT, THEY WON'T BITE YOU!"

THAT'S VERY FUNNY, MR. SACK

I ALWAYS LIKED THAT CARTOON

YOU'RE FUN TO BE WITH, MR. SACK

THANK YOU

IT'S GETTING LIGHT...THE SUN IS COMING UP...

I CAN'T LOOK! I CAN'T STAND THE SUSPENSE! BUT I HAVE TO LOOK! I HAVE TO KNOW! WILL I SEE THE SUN, OR WILL I SEE A BASEBALL? WHAT WILL I SEE?

!

What!. Me Worry?

GOOD GRIEF!

ANOTHER GAME TODAY... IF WE WIN, WE'LL ONLY BE TEN GAMES OUT OF SEVENTH PLACE...

WHY DO YOU ALWAYS PUT YOUR LEFT SHOE ON FIRST, BIG BROTHER?

WELL, ACTUALLY, I DON'T... I ONLY PUT IT ON FIRST ON DAYS WHEN WE HAVE A BASEBALL GAME...

I GUESS IT'S KIND OF A SUPERSTITION... BASEBALL PLAYERS HAVE A LOT OF SUPERSTITIONS.

WHAT WOULD HAPPEN IF YOU DIDN'T DO IT?

WHAT ARE YOU FISHING FOR, COMPLIMENTS?

HA HA HA HA HA HA HA!

I HATE JOKES LIKE THAT!

SO HERE WE GO ON A LITTLE PICNIC...

I BRING THE SALAD, THE SANDWICHES, THE PICKLES, THE POTATO CHIPS AND THE ROOT BEER...

WOODSTOCK BRINGS THE MARSHMALLOW!

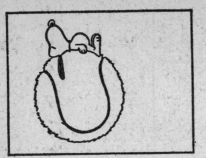

Her real name was Dorothy Fledermaus.

But all her friends called her "Dee."

Thus, she was frequently referred to as "Dee Fledermaus."

UH UH!

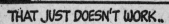

THAT JUST DOESN'T WORK..

I HAVE TO SLEEP IN THE SAME DIRECTION THAT THE WORLD TURNS

STILL MOPING? I CAN'T BELIEVE IT!

BUT THAT WAS ALMOST TEN WEEKS AGO!

I CAN'T HELP IT!

➤→

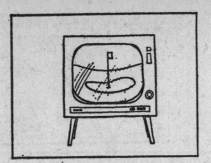

ALL RIGHT, GOLF FANS, THIS IS IT... THE OLD PRO HAS TO MAKE THIS ONE...

HE'S DOWN TO THE LAST PUTT, AND HE CAN'T PLAY IT SAFE... HE HAS TO GO FOR IT...

THERE'S NO TOMORROW!

THERE'S NO TOMORROW?!

THERE'S NO TOMORROW!!

THEY JUST ANNOUNCED ON TV THAT THERE'S NO TOMORROW!!!

THERE'S NO TOMORROW!! THEY JUST ANNOUNCED IT ON TV!

PANIC! PANIC! RUN! HIDE! FLEE! RUN FOR THE HILLS! FLEE TO THE VALLEYS! RUN TO THE ROOF TOPS!

SOMEHOW I NEVER THOUGHT IT WOULD END THIS WAY!

I THOUGHT ELIJAH WAS TO COME FIRST...

Though her husband often went on business trips, she hated to be left alone.

"I've solved our problem," he said. "I've bought you a St. Bernard. It's name is Great Reluctance."

"Now, when I go away, you shall know that I am leaving you with Great Reluctance!"

She hit him with a waffle iron.

HEY! HOW ABOUT HITTING ME A GROUNDER?

THAT'S FUNNY...
ACCORDING TO THIS,
YOUR TEMPERATURE
IS ONLY FORTY-TWO...

I DON'T
UNDERSTAND

SOMEBODY MUST HAVE
HAD COLD FEET!

THE WONDERFUL WORLD OF PEANUTS

☐	12544 6	What Next, Charlie Brown (26)	60p
☐	15135 8	You're the Greatest, Charlie Brown (27)	60p
☐	15829 8	It's For You Snoopy (28)	50p
☐	15828 X	Have It Your Way, Charlie Brown (29)	60p
☐	15698 8	You're Not For Real Snoopy (30)	60p
☐	15696 1	You're a Pal, Snoopy (31)	60p
☐	16712 2	What Now Charlie Brown (32)	60p
☐	17322 X	You're Something Special Snoopy (33)	60p
☐	17417 X	You've Got A Friend, Charlie Brown (34)	60p
☐	17844 2	Take It Easy, Charlie Brown (35)	60p
☐	17861 2	Who Was That Dog I Saw You With, Charlie Brown? (36)	60p
☐	18303 9	There's No-one like you Snoopy (37)	60p
☐	18663 1	Your Choice Snoopy (38)	60p
☐	18831 6	Try It Again Charlie Brown (39)	60p
☐	19550 9	You've Got It Made Snoopy (40)	60p
☐	19858 3	Don't Give Up Charlie Brown (41)	60p
☐	19927 X	You're So Smart Snoopy (42)	60p
☐	20491 5	You're On Your Own Snoopy (43)	60p
☐	20754 X	You Can't Win Them All Charlie Brown (44)	60p
☐	21236 5	It's All Yours Snoopy (45)	60p
☐	21797 9	Watch Out Charlie Brown (46)	60p
☐	21983 1	You've Got To Be You, Snoopy (47)	60p
☐	22159 3	You've Come a Long Way, Snoopy (48)	60p
☐	22304 9	That's Life Snoopy (49)	60p
☐	22778 8	It's Your Turn Snoopy (50)	60p
☐	22951 9	Play Ball Snoopy (51)	60p

Numbers 1-25 and all the above Peanuts titles are available at your local bookshop or newsagent, or can be ordered direct from the publisher, Just tick the titles you want and fill in the form below.
Prices and availability subject to change without notice.

CORONET BOOKS, P.O. Box 11, Falmouth, Cornwall.
Please send cheque or postal order, and allow the following for postage and packing:
U.K.—One book 22p plus 10p per copy for each additional book ordered, up to a maximum of 82p.
B.F.P.O. and EIRE—22p for the first book plus 10p per copy for the next 6 books, thereafter 4p per book.
OTHER OVERSEAS CUSTOMERS—30p for the first book and 10p per copy for each additional book.

Name ....

Address ....

....